A
GRAPHIC
MEMOIR

*Mansfield
and Me*

A
GRAPHIC
MEMOIR

Mansfield and Me

SARAH LAING

Lightning
Books ⚡

VICTORIA UNIVERSITY PRESS
Victoria University of Wellington
PO Box 600 Wellington
vup.victoria.ac.nz

First Published 2016
Reprinted 2017

A catalogue record for this book is available
from the National Library of New Zealand

ISBN 9781776560691

UK edition published 2017 by
LIGHTNING BOOKS
29a Barrow Street
Much Wenlock
Shropshire
TF13 6EN

ISBN 9781785630705

Published with the assistance of a grant from

ARTS COUNCIL OF NEW ZEALAND TOI AOTEAROA

Printed in China by 1010 Printing International

To Helen & Drew

~CONTENTS~

"Oh to be a _writer_
a real writer
given up to it
and to it alone! "

KATHERINE MANSFIELD
NOTEBOOK 38

When did I add Katherine Mansfield to my list of fascinating people? People I might become if I obsessed about them enough?

People along with:

OLGA
KORBUT
(Russian
Gymnast -
I wanted to
be her
when I
was 9)

MADONNA
(obsession
kicked in at 11,
when I saw
DESPERATELY
SEEKING SUSAN)

MORRISSEY
(I discovered
him at 16)

FRIDA
KAHLO
(I idolised her
at 19)

who fuelled
my desire
for greatness?

Perhaps it was seeded during our trips to York Bay

to visit my father's great aunts & uncle.

HI, GREAT GREAT AUNT ALISON!

COME ON IN

I'd spend our visits uncovering relics of old Wellington.

GOOD DRIVE SOUTH.

THE TRAFFIC WAS PRETTY LIGHT.

WHAT WAS THAT?

NOW THAT'S A DRAWING BY EDITH ROBISON

SHE WAS A FRIEND OF KATHERINE MANSFIELD'S. DO YOU KNOW OF HER?

UM... The Doll's House?

SHE WAS A NAUGHTY GIRL, THAT KATHLEEN.

* ANTHROPOSOPHY: A SYSTEM CREATED BY RUDOLF STEINER USING MAINLY NATURAL MEANS TO OPTIMISE PHYSICAL & MENTAL WELL-BEING

Until we got to Great Aunt Barbara & Great Uncle Ned's place.

Ned was a junk collector.

SO MANY TREASURES

His books had completely taken over the dining room.

While my parents drowned in tea, I tentatively fossicked.

GREAT AUNT ALISON MENTIONED THAT MRS ROBBIE WAS A FRIEND OF KATHERINE MANSFIELD'S

MANSFIELD? I'VE GOT BITS OF HER OLD HOUSE IN MY SHED. WHEN THE MOTORWAY CAME THROUGH I DROVE MY BEDFORD OVER TO FITZHERBERT TCE TO SALVAGE SOME.

& THE BEAUCHAMP ROPE TILES- I'VE GOT THOSE EDGING MY PATH.

Although Ned could wriggle his ears & raise one eyebrow there was a point at which he snapped.

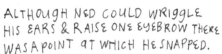

DON'T TOUCH THAT!

and I ran out...

Into the bush behind the houses

I was dragged out of the bush   And strapped into the car...

Granny's House   Rona Bay   Day's Bay   Sunshine Bay   Mahina Bay   York Bay

until we arrived at my grandmother's house...   where my parents would leave my sister & me...

and drive back to Palmerston North.

I tried on granny's dresses

I played Chinese checkers

& examined the writing box on top of Cousin Mildred.*

*(COUSIN MILDRED: 17th-C CABINET)

It was over 100 years old & had come from England.

If it was a sunny day Granny might take us for a swim.

She saved the bladders from her wine casks to use as flotation devices.

We'd drift out into the waves...

around
the bay
from
where
Katherine
Mansfield
and her
extended
family
took
their
summer
holidays
...

Born
Kathleen
Beauchamp
on 14 October
1888...

to Harold Beauchamp, "Pa Man", Bank Manager, son of an entrepreneur.

and the languid Annie, a beautiful Australian emigré, not really cut out for motherhood,

who left most of the parenting of their five children to Annie's mother, Margaret Mansfield Dyer.

14

Days Bay was also the place Katherine took Edith Bendall, aka Mrs Robbie from York Bay. Recently returned from Queen's College in London, Katherine was homesick for urban culture & befriended Edith, an artist who had trained in Sydney & wasn't as provincial as everyone else.

OH EDIE, I'M SO GRATEFUL FOR OUR WALKS— YOU'RE THE ONLY ONE WHO DOESN'T JUST TALK OF PARTIES & MARRIAGE.

GOD, I MISS LONDON. THAT'S WHERE LIFE IS— NOT HERE.

I'M HERE.

THANK CHRIST FOR THAT— I'D DIE IF YOU WEREN'T.

I LOVE YOU, KATIE— YOU'RE SO REFRESHING.

I CAN'T STAND THESE HEAVY SWIM SUITS.

LET'S SKINNY DIP— THERE'S NO ONE ELSE AROUND

I CAN'T BE HERE & NOT FEEL THE MAGIC OF HER BODY.

21

Her First Ball

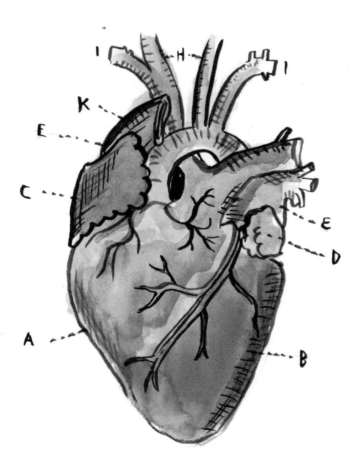

When I was a teen, my grand-mother moved to Palmerston North, to be nearer to us.

I'd go visit her after school while my mother was at work.

SHE TOOK UP A NEW HOBBY IN ACCORD WITH P.N.'s PLAINS:

HI, GRANNY

COME IN.

I'd try on all her old clothes,

which fitted me better now.

THIS ONE BELONGED TO MY MOTHER, KATHLEEN OTTERSON. FEEL HOW FINE THE VELVET IS? IT'S VERY OLD— PERHAPS 1920s.

& THIS ONE BELONGED TO MY NEIGHBOUR, LAVINIA WILLIS, WHO WAS SENT IT BY HER FRIEND, THE LORD MAYOR OF LONDON'S WIFE.

I had something a little more... spectacular in mind.

Perhaps more 'Sarah' from THE LABYRINTH

Or 'Andy' from PRETTY IN PINK.

Ball season was coming up at school.

Now girls, ball tickets are available in the common room at lunch time.

MANSFIELD Her First Ball

The only hitch was you had to come as a straight couple.

How are we meant to find boys to take to the ball at a single sex school? I never meet anyone.

To get us into the mood I've chosen Katherine Mansfield's *Her First Ball*. Sarah, will you read?

Me? OK.

JANET FRAME

I liked reading out loud. I planned on becoming an actor or a singer when I grew up.

Exactly when the ball began Leila would have found it hard to say. Perhaps her first real partner was the cab...

AND THESE PRETTY ARMS WILL HAVE TURNED INTO SHORT FAT ONES

AND YOU'LL BEAT TIME WITH SUCH a DIFFERENT KIND OF FAN — a BLACK EBONY ONE. AND YOU'LL SMILE AWAY LIKE THOSE POOR OLD DEARS UP THERE, AND POINT TO YOUR DAUGHTER

AND TELL THE ELDERLY LADY NEXT TO YOU HOW...

AND YOUR HEART WILL ACHE, ACHE, BECAUSE NO ONE WANTS TO KISS YOU NOW

SOME DREADFUL MAN TRIED TO KISS HER AT THE BALL

29

She was going through a divorce at the time — she was probably feeling desolate about love, wondering if she was too old to meet someone new.

And what was Katherine thinking when she wrote this? She was in Sierre, Switzerland. It was 1921, 18 months before her death.

IT'S SO RIDICULOUSLY BEAUTIFUL - LIKE THOSE LITTLE PAINTINGS ON MINERAL WATER BOTTLES.

She had full-blown tuberculosis and she was there for her lungs.

WILL I GET BETTER, HERR DOKTOR?

Hmm... IF YOUR DIGESTION CONTINUES GOOD, YOU STILL HAVE A CHANCE.

Although the Sierre was glorious, she didn't have the energy to walk.

She wrote stories furiously— some of her best - to sell.

IF ONLY I COULD TRAIN YOU NOT TO POOP ON THE CARPET.

Her husband John Middleton Murry was in London - he had work there & shied from sickness.

BY THE TIME JACK COMES I'LL TRAIN YOU TO PRESENT ARMS WITH MY FOUNTAIN PEN.

Mummy did come at the end of June, & they rented the Chalet des Sapins near Montana.

It was ideal for a while...

They worked mornings & read & smoked at night.

But as winter came Katherine found herself getting sicker.

Murry disappeared for hours, not telling her where he was.

* Katherine's cousin Elizabeth von Arnim, a popular author
* * Murry had an affair with Princess Bibesco, a writer and wife of a Romanian prince.

He was, in fact, at Elizabeth's, complaining about Katherine.

ONCE, IN A PIQUE, SHE WENT DOWN TO THE FRENCH FRONT & DELIBERATELY CAUGHT A VENEREAL DISEASE.

OH, MY

Katherine finished her mad flurry of story-writing in November, exhausted.

I HATE MYSELF FOR WASTING TIME. ALL THESE STORIES WILT & FADE WHILE I SIT HERE.

By December she was confined to bed.

WHY AM I HAUNTED BY THE NEARNESS OF DEATH?

Her friend Koteliansky had written to her about a Russian physician, Manoukhin

HE CLAIMS TO HAVE DISCOVERED A CURE FOR T.B. USING RADIATION.

JACK, I MUST TRY - I WANT TO WORK AGAIN.

HE SOUNDS LIKE A QUACK TO ME.

He refused to come to Paris with her, saying good bye in Sierre.

Instead she travelled with Ida, her companion.

The next day they went to see Manoukhin.

OH IDA, I DON'T KNOW IF HE'S A SAINT OR AN IMPOSTER—AND 300 FRANCS PER SÉANCE—WHERE WILL I FIND THAT MONEY?

WE'LL WORK SOME-THING OUT, KATIE.

THERE'S ALWAYS THE ROYALTIES FOR THE GARDEN PARTY...

She went back for her first séance out of fifteen.

I'M DONAT, MANOUKHIN'S COLLEAGUE. NOW TELL ME, ARE YOU CONSTIPATED?

WHAT DOES THAT HAVE TO DO WITH MY LUNGS?

The treatments gave her palpitations & made her feel nauseated.

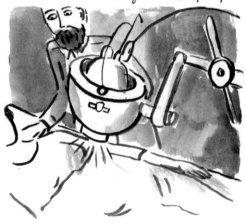

Manoukhin assured her that she was getting better.

But she was haunted by the picture of her heart, a heavy drop in her breast.

IS THIS WORTH IT AT ALL?

35

My heart, too, was a heavy drop on the night of the ball...

We lived over the road from the school, where the ball was held.

My parents had gone out, leaving me to babysit.

After the smell of smoke had subsided, I sat down to do my writing homework.

I finished at 11, when my parents came home.

YOU SHOULDN'T'VE SAID THAT TO LINDA.

WHY NOT? IT WAS TRUE.

WHAT'S THAT YOU'RE WORKING ON?

A STORY FOR SCHOOL

I CAN'T TAKE YOUR FATHER OUT.

CAN I SEE?

I watched him as he read, my body clenched in self-consciousness.

IT'S GOOD! VERY GOOD. THAT LINE ABOUT BEING A GAZELLE IS A BIT CLICHÉD BUT APART FROM THAT...

YOU HAVE A VERY NATURAL WAY OF WRITING.

WHY DO I SMELL SMOKE? & WHY IS TIMOTHY SLEEPING IN HIS CLOTHES?

I had made something out of my misery. And it was good. Perhaps I was a writer too.

THANKS, DAD.

SARAH!

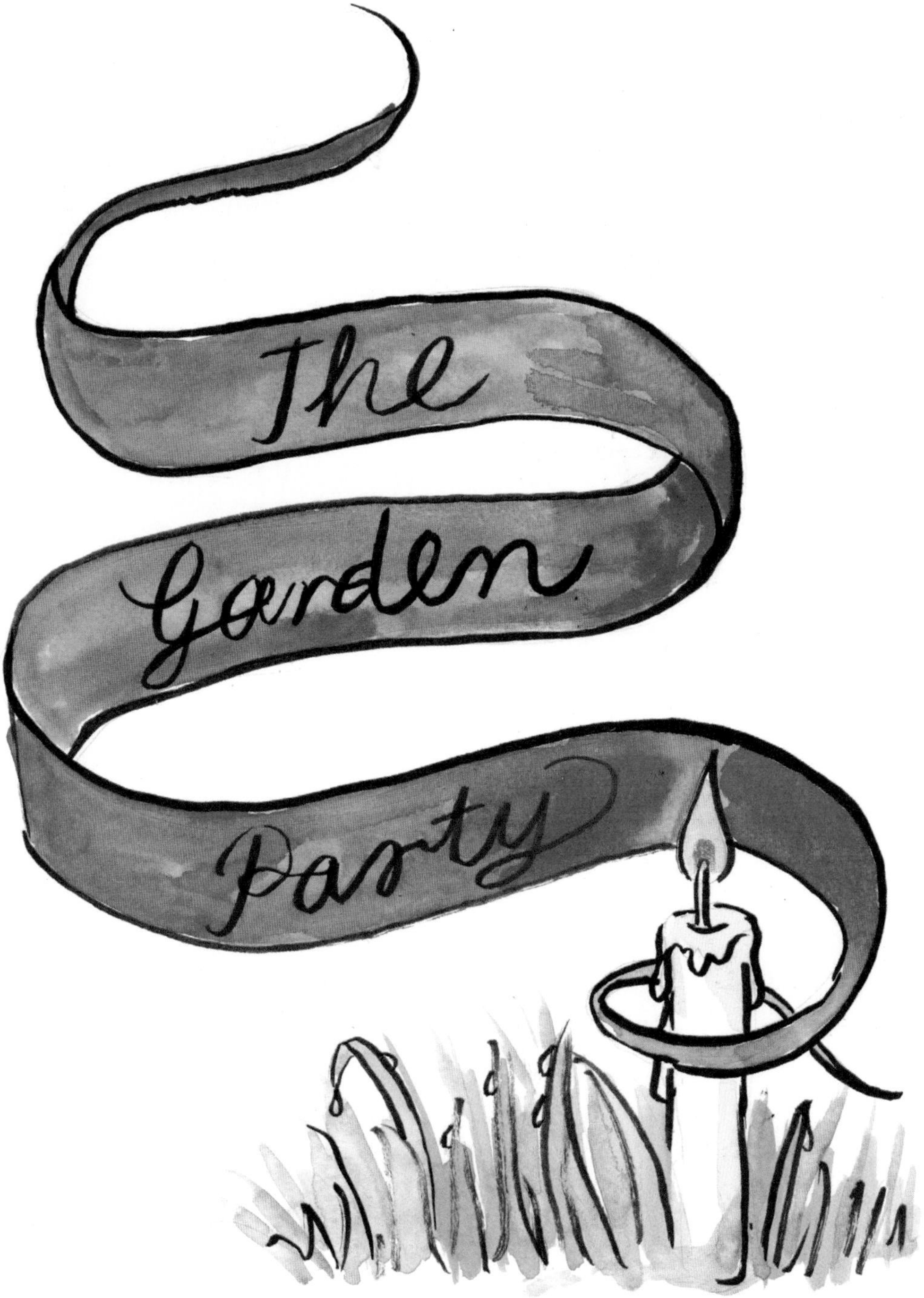
The Garden Party

My father had decided to stay in New Zealand rather than pursue a dazzling international career in science.

I loved Kiri Te Kanawa — she had sung 'O Mio Babbino Caro' in my favourite movie, A ROOM WITH A VIEW.

It formed a blueprint of my desire...

... and was the reason why I stole an Italian dictionary from a bookshop.

My mother loved Kiri Te Kanawa too...

...and so we set off on the drive down south to Trentham...

January was always a bit of a washout as far as summer went.

But thousands of people had been equally optimistic.

41

I drifted away from my family who were laying down the tarpaulin for the picnic...

...off into my own fantasies of me as an opera singer.

I had just begun singing lessons & I was sure that this was where my secret power lay

−this was my ticket out of this damp green country at the edge of the world.

But my fantasy was interrupted.

43

I found my family.

DID YOU SEE THE BABY?

WHAT BABY?

IT WAS ALL WHITE. THE PARAMEDICS WERE RUNNING WITH IT.

SOUNDS LIKE COT DEATH.

HOW AWFUL! I MISSED THAT.

HOW DID THEY NOT SEE IT? WHY ARE PEOPLE CARRYING ON AS IF NOTHING HAS HAPPENED?

I felt like Laura, from Katherine Mansfield's story THE GARDEN PARTY.

(Except Laura's weather was ideal.)

Laura's running around, bread & butter in her hand, helping with arrangements...

GOOD MORNING

...but then Godber's man, the one who brought the cream puffs, has some terrible news.

KNOW THOSE LITTLE COTTAGES BELOW HERE, MISS? WELL, THERE'S A YOUNG CHAP LIVING THERE, NAME OF SCOTT, A CARTER.

But just as the garden party went on, so did our concert.

She was so tiny, a bottle bobbing on an ocean of umbrellas.

and although her voice was beautiful, its secret message didn't reach me.

The rain abated as the concert drew to a close.

I couldn't stop thinking about the baby. And feeling like Kiri Te Kanawa was holding something back. She'd left us for so long, and this was what we were getting in return.

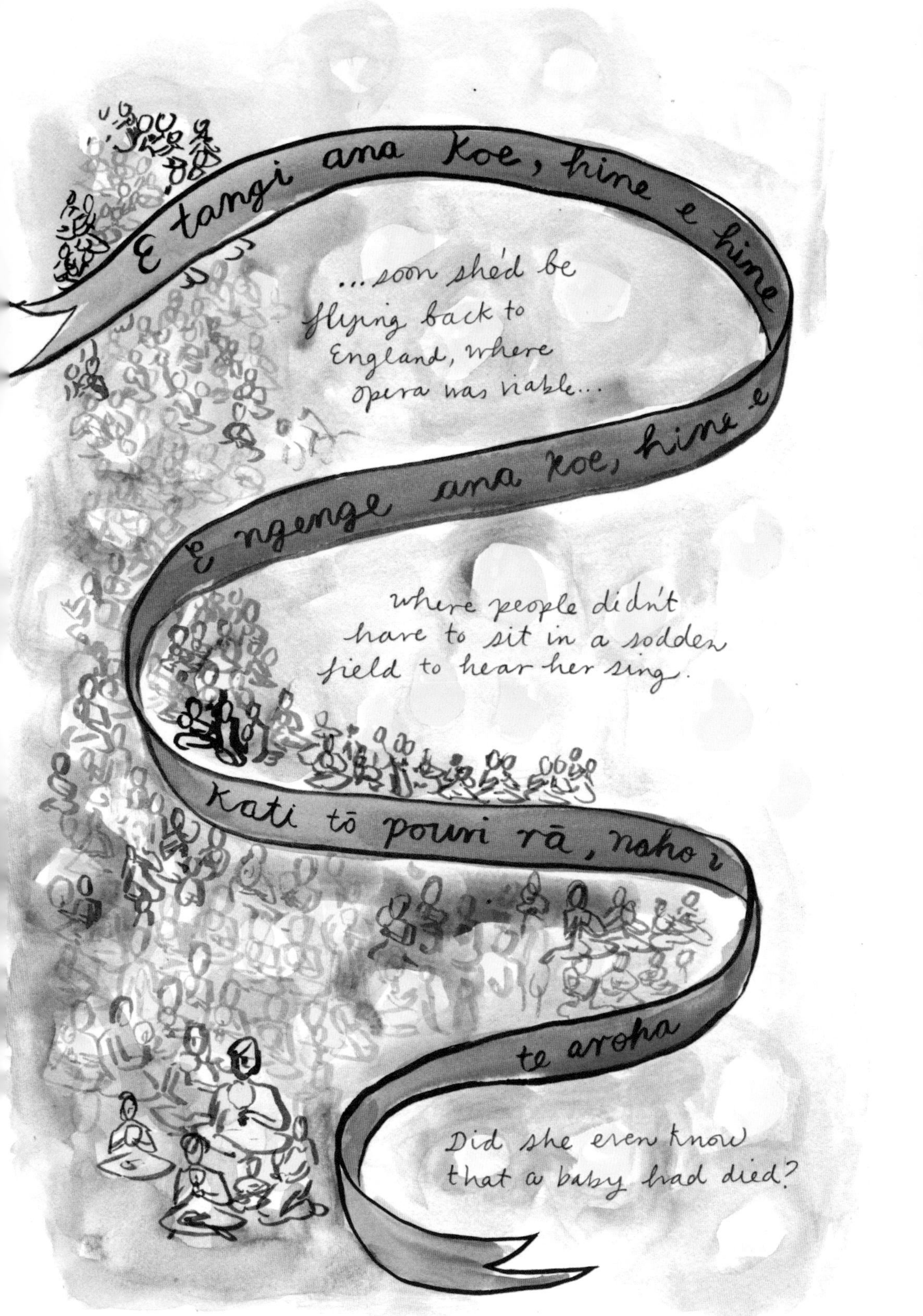

E tangi ana koe, hine e hine

...soon she'd be
flying back to
England, where
opera was viable...

E ngenge ana koe, hine e

where people didn't
have to sit in a sodden
field to hear her sing.

Kati tō pouri rā, noho i

te aroha

Did she even know
that a baby had died?

The journey to England took six weeks.

Ida Baker was there to meet her.

KATIE, DARLING, IT'S SO GOOD TO SEE YOU!

IDA!

BUT WHERE ARE YOUR RELATIVES? SURELY THEY'VE COME TO MEET YOU?

THEY'VE WASHED THEIR HANDS OF ME — I'M THEIR NAUGHTY COLONIAL COUSIN.

SOMEONE SHOULD'VE COME.

Katherine moved into the first floor of Beauchamp Lodge in Paddington.

LOOK, A BALCONY!

I HOPE IT WON'T BE TOO GLOOMY.

IT'S JUST LIKE BEING IN VENICE.

A few days later, Katherine went to visit the Trowells, a musical family from Wellington.

KATHLEEN—YOU'RE HERE! IT'S JUST LIKE OLD TIMES. I MISS HOME.

ARNOLD, GARNET, LOOK WHO'S COME TO VISIT!

KATHLEEN?

Katherine had fancied Arnold when she went for cello lessons in Wellington, but now that she was here...

GARNET— YOU'VE... CHANGED.

AND SO HAVE YOU.

They went out walking together.

PEOPLE MIGHT THINK THAT WE WERE MARRIED.

AND THAT WE LIVED IN ONE OF THOSE HOUSES & READ BOOKS IN FRONT OF THE FIRE

They practised being married.

Their investigations had consequences.

And garnet had to go away a lot, playing violin for a travelling opera company.

While he was away, she began singing lessons with George Bowden.

By the time garnet returned, Katherine was estranged from his family.

& garnet was beginning to waver.

Katherine turned her attentions to George Bowden, who she knew had fallen in love with her.

George proposed & Katherine accepted, marrying in a dirty Paddington registry office with Ida as her only guest.

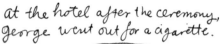
at the hotel after the ceremony, George went out for a cigarette.

I'LL BE BACK IN A FEW MINUTES. THIS IS YOUR CHANCE TO... MAKE YOURSELF COMFORTABLE.

WHAT HAVE I DONE?

HE REVOLTS ME. I'M STILL IN LOVE WITH GARNET.

BUT MY DEAR LADY, YOU'RE STILL DRESSED. THAT'S NOT HOW IT WORKS.

I CAN'T DO IT.

YOUR FRIGIDITY IS QUITE NORMAL— IT'S WEDDING NERVES. WOULD YOU LIKE A MASSAGE?

IT'S MORE THAN THAT.

NO!

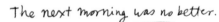
The next morning was no better.

I'LL MEET YOU AT THE FLAT—I HAVE A FEW THINGS TO PICK UP.

WE'LL BE MORE... COMFORTABLE THERE.

She never went to the flat. Instead she returned to Beauchamp Lodge...

BUT WHERE CAN I GO?

KATHERINE, THIS IS A LODGE FOR UNMARRIED WOMEN. I MUST ASK YOU TO LEAVE.

WHY NOT TO YOUR HUSBAND?!

Instead Ida helped her move into a flat above a hairdresser

THIS IS PRETTY GRIM

WE'LL SPRUCE IT UP – I'VE MY INHERITANCE

THE THING IS, I'M PREGNANT. I'M NOT SURE IF THIS IS THE PLACE FOR A BABY.

BUT – I THOUGHT YOU & GEORGE –

IT'S NOT GEORGE'S. IT'S GARNET'S.

At Ida's urging, she took the train to Glasgow to meet Garnet's opera company, The MOODY MANNERS.

MY LOVE!

LET ME TAKE THAT.

He was staying in a string of freezing, grotty lodges.

DO YOU HAVE ANY COAL?

KIPPERS, KATIE? SORRY I CAN'T OFFER YOU MORE.

SHALL WE GO TO THE PARK? YOU LOOK SO TIRED.

I'VE NO TIME, KATIE. THE ONLY WAY YOU'LL GET TO SEE ME IS BY JOINING THE CHORUS LINE.

54

and then the notice announcing Katherine's marriage was printed in The Times.

I CAN'T BELIEVE THAT YOU MARRIED & DIDN'T TELL ME!

GOD, YOU'RE SUCH A CONVENTIONAL MUMMY'S BOY. I'M SICK OF TRAILING AFTER YOU ANYWAY. THIS IS NO FUN.

She returned to London, to her squalid flat, to depression, to an addiction to Veronal* to help her sleep, to new attempts to write, more deeply this time.

In May, Katherine's mother arrived from New Zealand.

OH, THERE YOU ARE. WHAT AN APPALLING HAT. WE MUST GET RID OF IT.

HELLO, MOTHER.

I'M LIVING IN MAIDA VALE— WILL YOU STAY WITH ME?

DON'T BE RIDICULOUS— I'VE BOOKED A SUITE OF ROOMS ON MANCHESTER STREET.

TAKE THIS HAT.

THANK YOU, MA'AM

AND THIS, YOUNG LADY, IS NOT JAM TART FAT

ALTHOUGH YOU ALWAYS WERE A CHUBBY CHILD.

*VERONAL: a barbiturate used as a sleeping aid from 1903 to 1950s

She swept Katherine off to Bad Wörishofen, a spa town in Germany, to resolve her "health" issues.

I CAN'T BELIEVE YOU WERE SO FOOLISH. ESPECIALLY AFTER I GAVE YOU MY ABSOLUTE TRUST. YOU ARE A SILLY, SILLY GIRL.

I WASN'T SILLY—GARNET WAS WEAK.

Katherine moved into Pension Müller...

... to begin her treatment of bathing in the local waters, hosing, walking barefoot and eating a vegetarian diet.

She spent a lot of time in the arbour, drinking coffee and observing the other guests...

...who were to become the source material for her first book, 'In a German Pension'.

I EAT SAUERKRAUT WITH GREAT PLEASURE. BUT NOW THAT I'VE EATEN SO MUCH OF IT I CANNOT RETAIN IT & I MUST IMMEDIATELY RUSH TO THE BATHROOM

I'LL BE ABLE TO MANAGE ALONE... I'LL GET A WOMAN IN TO LOOK AFTER HIM SO I CAN WRITE...

HE'LL HAVE PEA GREEN EYES & A SHOCK OF DARK STANDING UP ON HIS HEAD...

BUT HOW WILL HE COME OUT? I KNOW THERE IS INTENSE PAIN - I REMEMBER MOTHER'S CRIES.

AND WHAT ABOUT THE ONE THAT DIDN'T MAKE IT, THE ONE GRANNY DYER SHOWED US, HER SKIN SO WHITE, HER EYES OPENED JUST ENOUGH TO SEE SLITS OF BLUE?

Katherine didn't realise she was in labour when she wrote to Garnet...

It's a recurring pain, it seems to diminish and then grow worse

OH GOD, HERE IT COMES AGAIN

She was all alone...

57

and six months was too
premature to survive

or even to be noted as a
stillbirth

aakgh!

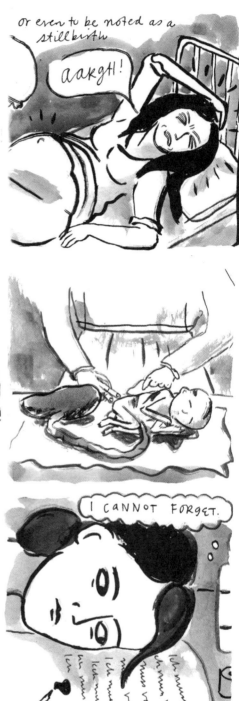

The baby was gone. As if it
never existed in the first place.

I MUST FORGET
ICH MUSS
VERGESSEN.
I MUST FORGET.

I CANNOT FORGET.

Prelude

My last year of high school, my two best friends were alternative music and English lit nerds.

None of us had boyfriends and we hadn't yet discovered alcohol and marijuana.

... so instead we got drunk on words.

MY ASPENS, DEAR, WHOSE AIRY CAGES QUELLED

QUELLED OR QUENCHED IN LEAVES THE LEAPING SUN

Our English teacher, too, got over-excited by them.

Prelud
KATHER

PRELUDE STARTED OFF AS THE ALOE. IT'S ABOUT THE BURNELLS, A FAMILY BASED ON MANSFIELD'S OWN, THE BEAUCHAMPS. STANLEY BURNELL IS BURSTING WITH VIRILITY.

GIRLS, LET US CONSIDER THE PASSAGE ON PAGE 23:

PUFF

OH DAMN! OH BLAST!

YOU LOOK LIKE A BIG FAT TURKEY

FAT! I LIKE THAT. I HAVEN'T A SQUARE INCH OF FAT ON ME.

IT'S ROCK— IT'S IRON.

LINDA BURNELL IS TOO DELICATE FOR ALL OF STANLEY'S ATTENTIONS, AND THEIR BYPRODUCT-BABIES. HER SISTER BERYL, ON THE OTHER HAND, IS UNMARRIED AND AWASH WITH DESIRE.

MANSFIELD COLL

OH, HOW TIRED I AM. VERY TIRED.

SOMEWHERE OUT THERE IS A YOUNG MAN, DARK & SLENDER, WITH MOCKING EYE, TIPTOEING THROUGH THE BUSHES, GATHERING THE FLOWERS INTO A BIG BOUQUET...

It sounded a little bit like my own furtive, lights-out fantasies.

THE ALOE, GIRLS, IS A PHALLIC SYMBOL— REPRESENTING WHAT LINDA FEARS.

The good thing about senior English was that we could now discuss sex.

DOES IT EVER HAVE FLOWERS? YES, KEZIA. EVERY HUNDRED YEARS.

NOW GIRLS, I HAVE PERMISSION SLIPS—WE'RE TAKING A TRIP TO WELLINGTON TO VISIT MANSFIELD'S BIRTHPLACE.

YAY!

ESCAPE FROM PALMERSTON!

62

We drove through the countryside, me not sitting with my two best friends, as they were slightly better friends with each other.

We were dropped off at a hostel on Tinakori Road.

The next morning we took the ferry across to Days Bay.

In the afternoon we visited her birthplace.

It was exhilerating to touch what Katherine once touched...

...but most things you couldn't touch—it was all cordonned off. She felt so remote—this could be any old house.

THAT DOESN'T SURPRISE ME.

I'M GLAD THEY SAVED THIS DRESS THOUGH - I ALWAYS DID LIKE IT.

NOT THAT I EVER CARED FOR THIS HOUSE - A DARK, OPPRESSIVE VICTORIAN THING, CRAMMED WITH PEOPLE & NICK-NACKS. I MUCH PREFERRED A JAPONISME-INSPIRED DECOR. AND WHO ARE THESE CRAZIES WHO'VE BEEN DREDGING UP MY TCHOTCHKES?

I'M PLEASED THEY FOUND THIS ROCKING HORSE THOUGH - VERA, CHADDIE & I USED TO FIGHT OVER WHO WAS GOING TO BE THE COW GIRL.

IF I BECAME A FAMOUS WRITER WOULD SOMEONE PUT MY SMITHS TAPES INTO A MUSEUM?

HEY, SARAH - WE'RE LEAVING NOW.

We rode home, all amped up.

DID YOU SEE THOSE PUNKS ON CUBA ST? THEY HAD A DALMATION. I WANT ONE.

I WANT TO LIVE IN WELLINGTON.

65

We decided to have a garden party at my place in honour of Katherine.

I asked my grandmother for props. She always had proper afternoon teas.

My grandmother had a 19th-Century shirt & skirt that I was allowed to wear, just this once.

In February 1912, Katherine invited John Middleton Murry over for their first tea party at her flat on Gray's Inn Road in London.

My father sent me off to the remote Ururweras in the hope that I'd so appreciate the beauty of my country that I'd change my mind about moving to London.

And I did — I was profoundly moved by it — but one cannot be an artist in New Zealand...

...no matter how astonishing it is.

YOU MUST WRITE MORE STORIES SET IN YOUR HOMELAND

I WILL — I MISS IT SO.

Our teacher had the same advice.

SOME OF MANSFIELD'S MOST FAMOUS STORIES WERE BASED ON HER CHILDHOOD—THAT'S WHAT YOU SHOULD CONSIDER WRITING ABOUT—WRITE WHAT YOU KNOW.

POETRY COMPETITION

THINK ABOUT THIS IF YOU'RE PLANNING ON ENTERING THE POETRY COMPETITION.

My friends were definitely going to enter.

I'VE GOT A SARTRE PARODY POEM I'M WORKING ON.

SOMETIMES I WAKE UP TO WRITE POEMS AT 2AM BECAUSE THAT'S WHEN THE BEST LINES COME

Although I'd written poems for the previous year's writing portfolio, I hadn't written any since.

I DON'T THINK I'LL ENTER—I'M NOT A POET ANYWAY.

But the day before the competition closed:

I'M ASSUMING YOU'RE ENTERING, SARAH. YOU MUST HAVE PLENTY OF POEMS UP YOUR SLEEVE.

UM, MAYBE?

After school I began writing

THIS IS PRETTY SHIT

Messy, raw, surrealist,
disastrous poems exploded
out of me.

But then I started thinking
about Great-Great Aunt Alison

And our visits to York Bay

It was official – I was a poet.

I bought myself a notebook

and decorated it.

If inspiration struck in the middle of the night I would wake up and write stuff down.

The summer I
left highschool,
I finally found
my first boyfriend.

I had my first kiss in
my empty highschool grounds

I felt my first erection
under his parents' feijoa tree

CLINK

after a night of drinking home-brewed elderflower wine,

dancing to Latin American tapes on the stereo

and looking at stars in a neighbouring rugby field

I lost my virginity.

We decided to move in together so we could do it less furtively. A friend of my boyfriend's was living in a huge villa, recently relocated from my street to the countryside. He needed flatmates, and I had always wanted to live in a house with a verandah.

We went to inspect our new room.

WHAT AN AMAZING VIEW

IT'S BEAUTIFUL.

MORRISSEY 1991

So WHAT DO YOU THINK?

WE LOVE IT.

GREAT. WHEN DO YOU WANT TO MOVE IN?

as SOON as POSSIBLE.

IT'S MEANT TO BE- EVERY TIME I WALKED PAST THIS HOUSE I THOUGHT 'I WANT TO LIVE THERE'.

YEAH, IT IS PRETTY GREAT. Sam's a good EGG- BUT HE CAN GET INTENSE. YOU KNOW -THIS IS A SECRET- HE WAS INTO AUTO-EROTIC ASPHYXIATION. ONCE HE almost KILLED HIMSELF.

WOaH.

We moved in the following weekend.

Sam had a friend over.

Then another friend turned up.

He had a dog too.

81

In April 1916, Katherine and John moved to the country too.

I'M NOT SURE I LIKE THIS LANDSCAPE—IT'S ALL BOULDERS

IT'LL BE MARVELOUS, TIG. FRESH AIR, VIGOROUS WALKS—OUR LITTLE COTTAGE IN THE COUNTRY AND THE LAWRENCES WILL BE FINE INTELLECTUAL COMPANY.

NOT FRIEDA

Frieda, an earthy German woman, had left her husband and three children to be with DH Lawrence.

WHAT THE HELL HAVE I LET MYSELF IN FOR?

KATHERINE, YOU EXQUISITE CREATURE—I'M SO PLEASED YOU'RE HERE.

FRIEDA—IT'S LOVELY TO SEE YOU AGAIN.

She still grieved for them.

84

OH, WHAT FUN WE'LL HAVE- YOU'LL BE IN THE COTTAGE NEXT TO US WITH THE TOWER ROOM. YOU'LL BE ABLE TO GET CRACKING ON THE DOSTOEVSKY- I'M WRITING ANOTHER NOVEL- IT'S EARLY DAYS BUT...

Mumy and Laurence went tramping across the hills together.

CENTRAL TO ALL EXPERIENCE IS SEX- AND THAT'S WHY I LOVE FRIEDA - SHE'S SO PRIMAL & PASSIONATE. HOW IS KATHERINE IN THE SACK?

OH- WELL- HER HEALTH IS RATHER DELICATE AT THE MOMENT- BUT SHE CAN BE VERY INVENTIVE.

Katherine languished, rereading her story THE ALOE, listening to the rain.

THIS HARDLY FEELS REAL TO ME ANYMORE.

PLOP

THESE GREY STONES; THAT GREY SEA... KARORI COULDN'T BE FURTHER AWAY

AND LAWRENCE, HE'S LIKE A BIG BLACK STEAM ENGINE WITH HIS MOODS- AWAY HUFFING AND SNORTING.

LOOK AT THEM- EITHER FIGHTING OR SHAGGING

Although Katherine wasn't getting much done, Laurence was writing WOMEN IN LOVE.

GUDRUN... CHARMING, SO INFINITELY CHARMING AND ALSO VERY BEAUTIFUL.

Gudrun was based on Katherine

SHE OBSERVES PEOPLE WITH OBJECTIVE CURIOSITY.

An artist, not a writer, Gudrun shared Katherine's sang-froid and bareness of manner. Her dress sense was unmistakable

He based the character Gerald on Murry, using the wrestling match that they'd had behind locked doors...

...as a scene in the novel.

THERE IS SOME INVIOLABLE
SACRAMENT BETWEEN US—

SOME
PRE-CHRISTIAN
BLOOD-
RITE

IN KEEPING WITH THE
PRIMEVAL ROCKS
ABOUT
US—

DON'T YOU THINK?

Although Murry had started off enjoying himself, he began to share Katherine's concerns about Lawrence's erratic behaviour.

89

By the end of May, Katherine & John could no longer maintain the charade. They left for another seaside cottage in early June.

Laurence did not say goodbye.

I wasn't entirely sure of what I made of the countryside

I wasn't doing much writing either. I had an intoxicating list of books for my Women's Literature course at University

The flat started off well

We cooked flat dinners together

Sometimes Sam would invite us to hang out in his room.

It took me a while to figure out exactly what I was looking at...

...since it was my first glimpse of digital porn.

Sam started spending longer and longer shut up in his room

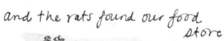

and the rats found our food store

One night, returning late from university, we met a problem bigger than the rats.

We drove as close to the house as we could.

As we lay in bed we could hear them grinding their horns against the weatherboards.

By the time the farmer came to get them, the garden was trashed.

And then the water ran out.

He called a flat meeting.

We found a new flat pretty soon after that.

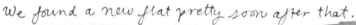

Sam did not say goodbye.

New Friends

I hadn't wanted to go to my hometown University, Massey.

I'd wanted to move to Wellington and go to Victoria...

...but the government had just hiked the fees & cut allowances and my parents wouldn't pay for it.

I was drawn to the alternative students - the punks, the goths, the grungy kids...

...the ones who DJ'd at Radio Massey and moshed at the student union gigs.

There was one particular woman I was curious about, someone that I recognized from my Rennaissance & Romantic literature classes. She seemed to be friends with half the alternative crowd, somehow at the centre of things.

I always felt like I was on the outer edge.

I never knew if I should be outraged or pleased that she had my T-shirt, but I figured we must have something in common.

HEY, LOOK, SHE HAS THE SAME T-SHIRT as you.

MORRISEY 1991

One day I saw her sitting with my highschool friends.

I hadn't written anything decent in ages.

I was super excited to be invited, even by proxy—this was my in to the alternative crowd.

The only other group I'd been part of was the local youth orchestra, and even then I wasn't part of the cool kids' gang.

In July 1916 Katherine was invited to Garsington, where the Bloomsbury Group met. She worried about how false she'd been in her letters to Lady Ottoline Morrell, and which 'self' she might be amongst the cultural heavyweights who gathered there.

Katherine had been introduced to Ottoline by D.H. Lawrence, but she hosted all kinds of people at her Oxfordshire manor...

...including BERTRAND RUSSELL: philosopher, mathematician & social critic

LYTTON STRACHEY: author, critic

DORA CARRINGTON: artist

ALDOUS HUXLEY: writer

Maria Nys, Aldous' girlfriend

and DOROTHY BRETT, painter.

One evening...

AMAZING GRACE, HOW SWEET THE SOUND

SHE HAS A RATHER LOVELY VOICE, N'EST-CE PAS? SO LOW & HUSKY

I'VE HEARD SHE'S INTO FREE LOVE

SWING LOW, SWEET CHARIOT...

SNIGGER

OH, COME ON!

BRAVO!

DON'T STOP!

THEY WEREN'T LAUGHING AT YOU, KATHERINE— YOU WERE MARVELLOUS. THEY WERE GOSSIPING AMONGST THEMSELVES.

I WILL NEVER BELONG HERE.

The picnic hadn't catapaulted me into friendship with the girl with the same T-shirt, but now I knew where she lived.

I psyched myself up to become proper friends with her

Wednesday was when my boyfriend went to his Latino band practice.

I was amazed at how much she was willing to tell me....

MY FIRST REAL BOYFRIEND LIKED TO PRETEND HE WAS A VAMPIRE.

HE USED TO HIDE IN THE COAT CLOSET...

AND LEAP OUT AT ME AS I CAME THROUGH THE DOOR.

...and how much she'd lived while I'd been reading my dad's Stephen King books and throwing garden parties.

I REFUSED TO HAVE SEX WITH HIM UNTIL I TURNED 16 - ALL MY FRIENDS WERE HAVING SEX ALREADY

I WAS A VIRGIN UNTIL I WAS 18

THERE WAS THIS GUY I KNEW WHO HAD A DOG AS HIS GIRLFRIEND - AT PARTIES HE'D HAVE HER SIT BESIDE HIM, HIS FINGERS IN THE DOG'S VAGINA

UGHH, GROSS!

I'M SO BORING AND MIDDLE-CLASS - HOW CAN I BE A WRITER IF I HAVEN'T REALLY EXPERIENCED ANYTHING YET?

I WASTED A LOT OF WRITING TIME IN PURSUIT OF EXPERIENCE

MISSEY

By June, 1917, Lytton Strachey had engineered a meeting between Katherine and Virginia Woolf.

Dear Katherine
I should be delighted if you would join me for supper.
Virginia

NO, THIS WON'T DO

BETTER. PERHAPS A SHAWL

THIS WILL SCARE HER A BIT

Over the spring and summer of 1917, Katherine and Virginia's friendship grew.

122

I remember
everything

By the time I was twenty, I had managed to move to Wellington. I finished my Bachelor of Arts there, and my boyfriend and a few Massey friends shifted south soon after my final exams.

I'd imagined, post-graduation, that I'd get a job as an editor, or a trainee diplomat for the Ministry of Foreign Affairs

but it didn't work out that way.

I was fired from the laundry factory pretty quickly

...for pointing out my boss' oversights.

UM, DID YOU KNOW IT'S ILLEGAL NOT TO PAY STAT HOLIDAYS?

WHY DON'T YOU COME UP TO MY OFFICE FOR A CHAT

I got my hair cut off to test my hypothesis

My boyfriend was not impressed.

and despite all the applications I sent out I could not find a job.

Helen and I enrolled ourselves in the creative writing night class at the local high school.

Our teacher was a middle-aged lesbian who'd once been married & her stories explored the seismic shift in her life.

I remembered my sister as a one-year-old, when I was almost four.

afterwards we had to read.

Each week we had homework.

There was an article in <u>Interview</u> Magazine, about up-and-coming women writers who lived in New York City. I cut out their pictures and pasted them into my journal for inspiration. One day that would be me.

13/6/94

I was going to write on the computer + that crisp efficiency, that logic. Never an illegeable scrawl or an embarasses scribble to disguise a clumsy sentense. I feel scared to write, now that I know I must read this to the class. Is it witty? Is it poignant enough? I know I must give myself permission to write rubbish, but at what cost? I feel as though people in the class ha no respect for me, they think I'm silly and frivolous compared to Brenda and Helen, who can write about painful things. What do I have to write that is painful? What painful to me is myself; my inadequacies, my fear of failure, my fear that I'm a boring, stupid unoriginal person. Doesn't that person in the bath look beautyful?

"Two long years I sat there, like an idiot eating their shit while they snuck off and fucked in the bathroom on holidays"
by Elissa Schappell

The course had an element of group therapy in it

WRITE WHAT'S PAINFUL. IT'S THERE YOU'LL FIND YOUR BEST WRITING - WHAT WILL REALLY MOVE READERS. KEEP PUSHING THROUGH

WHAT AM I GOING TO WRITE ABOUT? NOTHING TRULY PAINFUL HAS HAPPENED TO ME, UNLESS YOU COUNT BEING DIAGNOSED WITH DIABETES ON MY NINTH BIRTHDAY.

DOES THAT EVEN COUNT?

KATHERINE MANSFIELD DIDN'T START WRITING HER BEST NEW ZEALAND STORIES UNTIL HER BROTHER WAS KILLED IN WWI

SOMETHING DRAMATIC NEEDS TO HAPPEN FOR YOUR ALCHEMICAL TRANSFORMATION FROM SCRIBBLER TO REAL WRITER. IT DOESN'T JUST TAKE A NICE TURN OF PHRASE.

And yet, despite all my trepidation, the next time I read, something good happened.

...multicoloured veins plunging into the ocean...

YOU WILL BE A WRITER.

I basked in the pronouncement...

...intoning it as I fought with my boyfriend...

NO, I WON'T BUY YOU A DRINK YOU OWE ME

GOD YOU'RE A STINGY BASTARD

OH IT'S YOU THAT I

LOVE AND IT'S TRUE THAT I

and ultimately decided to move out.

I SHOULD GET THE TABLE - I FOUND IT

AND I PAID FOR IT, REMEMBER?

I found a room in a flat in Thorndon, down a tiny lane off Tinakori Road, the street where Katherine Mansfield had lived as a child.

I WONDER IF THESE ARE THE WORKMEN'S COTTAGES FROM "The garden Party"?

The former occupant of my room had left a picture of Morrissey pinned in the closet.

I set up my writing box & the computer I'd wrangled off my ex-boyfriend

and began to explore the house where I'd spend the next eighteen months of my life.

In August 1915, Katherine got a visitor—her brother Leslie, stationed at Aldershot as part of the British army.

134

fig. 1.

fig. 2.

fig. 3.

136

and then, in October, the telegram arrived.

POST OFFICE TELEGRAPHS

If the receiver of an Inland Telegram doubts its accuracy he may have it repeated on payment of half the amount originally paid for its transmission,

Lombard St Handed in at 6·16 Received here at 6·35

To Mrs Mansfield Murra
5 acacia Rd St Johnwood
Deeply regret inform you Leslie
killed 7th come and see
me Kay

IT CANNOT BE TRUE IT CAN
NOT BE TR   IT CANNOT
BE TRUE IT   TRUE IT CA
NNOT BE   CANNOT
BE TRUE IT C OT BE TRUE
IT CANNO   IT CANNOT
BE TRUE   IT CAN
NOT BE   TRUE

Mr Kay dispensed Katherine's small monthly income from her father.

MR KAY

KATHERINE
—COME
IN

I'M SO SORRY,
IT IS TRUE
MY DEAR

NO.

Dear Mr Mansfield

I very much regret I
have been unable to write you before in reply
to your last letter, but we have had very little
time to ourselves having to fight another
foe now besides the Germans, the weather.
You ask me if Leslie spoke before
he died, & if he knew he was going to
die. I can answer yes to each
question.

He was heard to say several times
"God forgive me for all I have done" & then
just before he died he asked that his
head might be raised as he could not
breath.

After that, about ten minutes
the moment of the accident, he died from
Doctors send, in cases where the inj
were as terrible as his were, there

B.E.F.
France
13·11·15

139

140

So here I was, in the place where Katherine was once happy. Or, technically, over the road from it, as her house had been pulled down to make way for the motorway.

My friend Drew, accustomed to heartbreak, encouraged me to drown my sorrows.

I was drunk on the notion that I was crossing some threshhold of experience, one that would unite me with some of my heroes.

I didn't confess that this was my first time with a woman

I was grateful for my k d lang poster, which gave me an air of legitimacy.

In the morning it was obvious that we were unsuited for each other.

I could have told her she'd left off a number

But I think she already knew.

Giddy with lack of sleep, I put on my work clothes to walk up to my new job as a secretary.

Katherine didn't think Tinakori Road was a fashionable street, although it was now.

HOW WILL I FUNCTION AT WORK TODAY?

"It was a little trying to have one's washerwoman living next door who would persist in attempting to talk to Mother over the fence", she wrote in her journal.

And then there was the "endless family of halfcastes who appeared to have planted their gardens with empty jam tins and old saucepans & black iron kettles."

CAN YOU TYPE THIS FOR ME URGENTLY?

But this was where she felt she must write about to keep her brother alive.

I HAVE GOT TO GET OUT OF HERE. I DIDN'T GET A DEGREE TO BE A SECRETARY.

In November 1915, Katherine moved to France. She didn't feel like she could write in Accacia Road, with all those memories, and the damp, and the cold.

Alone in her hotel room, crippled with an acute case of rheumatism, Katherine thought & dreamt about her brother obsessively, re-imagining her New Zealand childhood.

Slowly the pain in Katherine's hip began to subside.

And the story, the one that started with the birth of her brother, began to emerge.

Indiscreet Journeys

Design school started off promisingly.

I signed up for 2d & 3d design...

and photography

154

I took the night train to Auckland, where the rest of my family had moved, but somewhere along the tracks a tree trunk had fallen

and we were transferred to a bus.

My parents picked me up, 14 hours after I'd left Wellington, six years since I'd first left home.

In February 1915, dissatisfied with John's emotional frigidity, Katherine took a trip to France to visit writer and postman-corporal Francis Carco.

Katherine had first met Francis Carco through John, when they moved to Paris in 1913.

162

what is the
point of this
war at all?

164

There was so much talk, the sex they had was almost incidental.

and then he was gone and Katherine returned to Paris

Katherine wrote about her experience in a story called "An Indiscreet Journey."

Francis Carco wrote about his, weaving her letters and words into his novel, "Les Innocents."

I began writing again too...

TAP TAP TAP

TAP TAP TAP

While my family fretted about me.

I DON'T THINK SHE'S BEEN LOOKING AFTER HERSELF

SHE HAS PUT ON WEIGHT

SHE HAS TO FIND a JOB. I DON'T WANT AN aDULT CHILD LIVING HERE RENT-FREE

I wasn't writing about my most recent fuck-ups.

22,321 WORDS!

Instead I was excavating my first relationship for novel material.

As the page numbers grew, so did my fantasies of fame.

SO TELL ME, SARAH— WHEN DID YOU FIRST KNOW THAT YOU WERE A WRITER?

IT ACTUALLY TOOK ME A WHILE TO FIGURE IT OUT.

PAVEMENT

SARAH LAING: WRITER

I'd write for 2 hours every morning in the freezing study

and in the afternoon I'd look for a job.

Flies in the milk jug

I returned to Wellington two years later on account of a man. We'd met as flatmates in Thorndon, and had fallen into bed with each other after a few big nights out. We'd discounted each other as boyfriend/girlfriend material - he was ten years my senior and I was possibly a lesbian. And yet, we had so much to talk about - music, books, movies, food, philosophy, politics. I couldn't stop thinking about him. I moved in with him in 1998. That was the year Helen came back from her Big O.E.

LONDON WAS amazing BUT SO INTENSE. I WENT ON a BLOOMSBURY PILGRIMAGE - HOGARTH PRESS, THE omega WORKSHOPS - SO MUCH HISTORY.

173

We met in Aro Valley

where all the artists lived

So everybody needs to pick a post card out of the box & we'll spend 10 minutes writing about it.

FLICK
FLKK

WOMEN'S

SCRITCH
SCRITCH

SCRITCH
SCRITCH

NOW WE'RE GOING TO GO ROUND THE TABLE & READ

I was pleased with my poem — it had come out fully formed.

The Trapeze girl learns to type. She's sick of sequins — they dig into her thighs and leave ghost fish scales.

NICE! MY TURN: You walk, Jasmine, trailing behind you

HIPPY

We left energised

WE'LL HAVE TO PERFORM AT THE CUBA ST. OPEN MIKE NIGHT

WE CAN'T JUST WAIT FOR FAME TO HAPPEN TO US

THAT COULD BE FUN

I began writing poetry every night after work...

SCRITCH
SCRITCH

SCRITCH

... to be performed.

In the dark of night she pushes open her caravan door and runs

Helen had a poem about Frida Kahlo's abscesses which she drained into jars

It always got people's attention.

But her poems changed when she got pregnant

BRING ME A SEA BABY WRAPPED IN SEA KELP

And her pregnancy made me anxious.

BARREN AUNTIE, KNIT-ONE, PEARL-ONE, MAKING CASINGS FOR BABIES PALE AS PEELED GARLIC

Because there was always someone random at the open-mike, we decided to get our own gig.

THEN RIPPED HER PANTIES OFF AT THE TRIAGE STATION & UP SPRUNG HER DICK

We found a Hawaiian-themed bar willing to host our fringe show

and set about roping in our friends

YOU PLAY THE DOUBLE BASS, RIGHT?

ER- I DID- IN HIGHSCHOOL

Nicki wasn't so into the Beat Poet Vibe so he found a drum circle

I designed some post cards with our poems on the back

POETRY FOR REAL

I'LL DROP THEM AROUND TOWN- WE'LL BE TOTALLY FAMOUS

And I photocopied poems at my work that we could make into books.

Everybody came over to my house.

HI! HEY

and we collated our edition of chapbooks to sell at the show

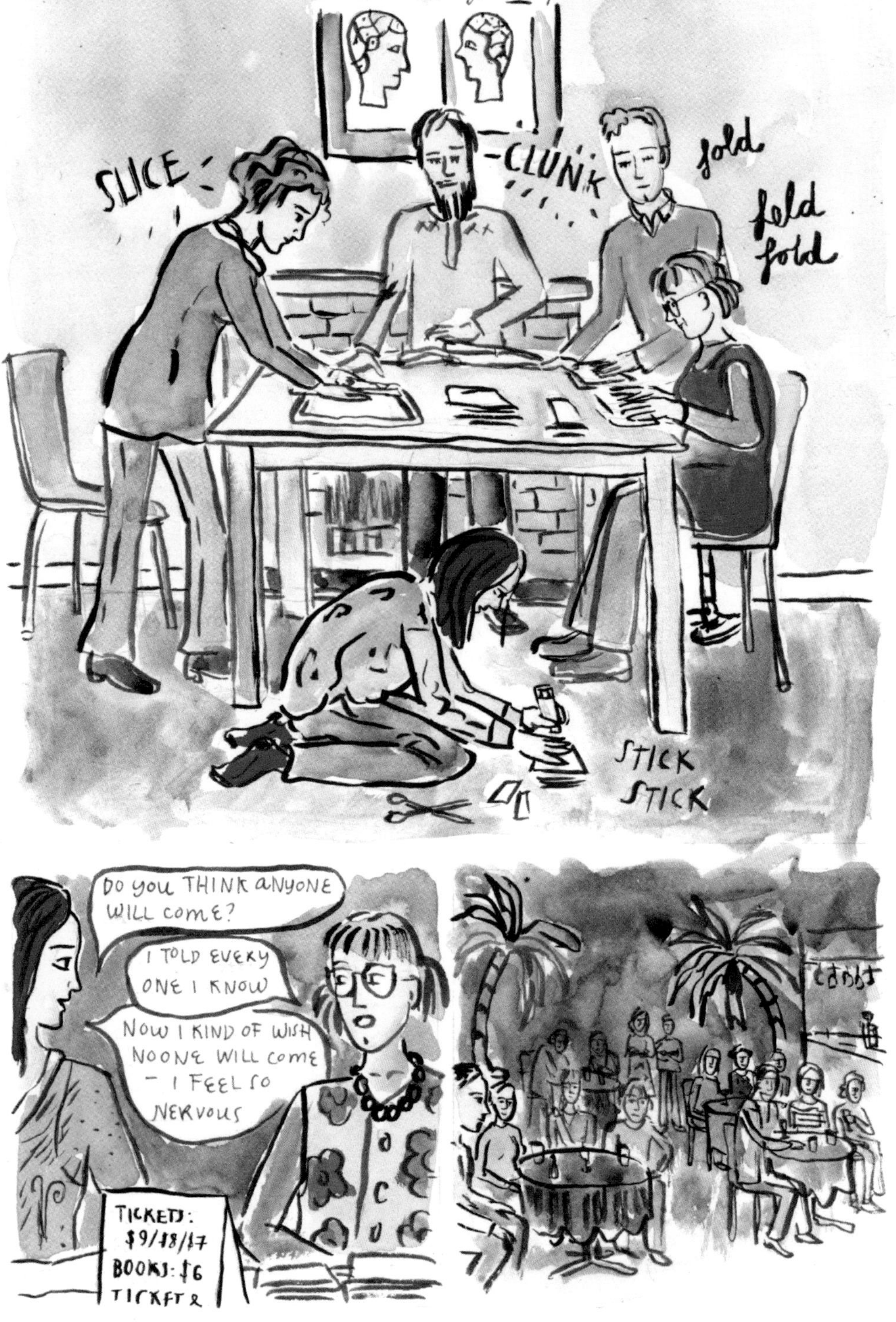

But it went really well.

In June 1917, Virginia approached Katherine with a proposal:

183

Late August, Katherine arrived at Asheham, where the Woolfs spent some of their time

A CITY HOUSE, A COUNTRY HOUSE, AN INDEPENDENT INCOME, A STEADFAST HUSBAND — IT'S ALL A BIT MUCH REALLY.

CAN I CONTAIN MY JEALOUSY OR WILL IT SEEP OUT FROM BEHIND MY MASK?

I HOPE THEY LIKE 'PRELUDE'.

SO WONDERFUL THAT YOU COULD COME! LYTTON STRACHEY'S HERE TOO — WE SHALL HAVE A MARVELLOUS WEEKEND

MRS MURRY — EVERYTHING IS BETTER NOW YOU'RE HERE. WOULD YOU LIKE TO GO MUSHROOM HUNTING?

I HAVEN'T DONE SO SINCE I WAS A CHILD

185

The flowers come in as a bright dazzle

an exquisite
haunting scent

a shape
so formal
and fine

so much a flower
of the mind

I see
pairs of
people —
they must
be different

There must
be a slight air
of enchantment

a kind of, musically
speaking, conversation
set to flowers

Katherine made for Bandol in the south of France on her own, remembering what a blissful, productive time she'd had when she'd stayed there with John. Only this time, John had war work in London, and Ida couldn't get the necessary documents to enter France. When Katherine arrived, everything was different.

191

192

195

On February 18, 1918, Katherine experienced her first haemorrhage

PERHAP

TO

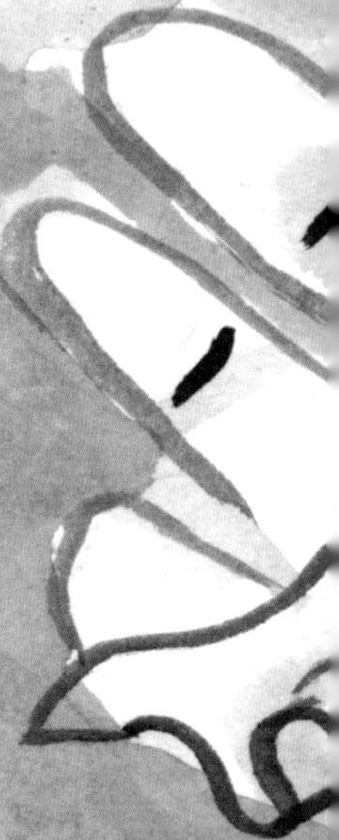

AND I
SHAN'T
HAVE MY
WORK WRITT

THAT'S WHAT MATTERS

How unbearable would it be to die, leave 'scraps', 'bits',

NOTHING REAL FINISHED

Bombardment

Emboldened by our Fringe Festival success, Helen and I
decided to stage another show the following year.

IT DOESN'T HAVE
TO BE POETRY THIS
TIME - I SAW THIS amazing
STORY-TELLING SHOW
WITH MULTIMEDIA

WE COULD BE IN THE
BAND OURSELVES THIS TIME

AND WE'LL MAKE
A ZINE TO GO WITH IT

WE CAN
WRITE STORIES
ON A THEME
AND PERFORM
THEM

WHAT THEME?
MORRISSEY?
ROAD TRIPS?
FEMINISM?
PUNK?

POP MUSIC?

2001 was shaping up to be a big year. I had a job at a fancy design studio, I'd signed up for more creative writing classes; and Jonathan and I were saving money to move to New York City.

Even though my job was intense, my boss was supportive of my "hobbies."

He'd been in a punk band before he became a company director.

I was really proud of our zine, even if it wasn't the hand-pasted, photocopied, DIY punk original.

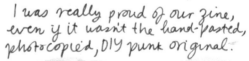

And I was even prouder of our performance – we were funny, confessional, eloquent and rock'n'roll.

In the meantime, my grandmother was growing frailer. I visited her whenever I was in Auckland and assumed she'd always be there, struggling out of her Honda Civic after a game of croquet, playing demon patience and drinking sherry.

Her stories, always quite meandering, grew harder to follow.

My father, conscious that she was the repository of the family history, encouraged her to talk into a tape recorder.

But he was unwilling to interview her, and without a live audience, her stories petered out.

RING RING

HI MUM ...YOU'RE WHERE?

SHOULD I FLY NORTH? OKAY, OKAY. WELL, LET ME KNOW

WHAT'S THE STORY?

IT'S MY GRANDMOTHER

SHE'S HAD A MASSIVE STROKE. SHE'S IN WHANGAREI HOSPITAL

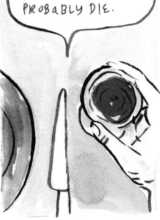

MUM SAYS SHE WILL PROBABLY DIE.

LOOK, I'M WEARING HER AMBER BEADS TODAY. WEIRD.

SHE'S GIVEN ME SO MANY THINGS OVER THE YEARS

207

Granny'd been staying at my uncle and aunt's in the Far North when she had her stroke.

My uncle had to pull out his new olive tree plantation so the helicopter could land.

The woman layed out in the funeral parlour looked nothing like her.

and although my cousins seemed to know what to do

GOODBYE, GRAN

I did not.

IS IT BECAUSE SHE'S NOT WEARING GLASSES? OR BECAUSE HER CHEEKS HAVE SUNK INTO THEIR POCKETS?

I read my poem at the funeral

...GRANNY WOULD PEER, NOSE BEAD POISED TO DROP IN DEFIANCE OF HER LACE-EDGED HANKY

afterwards we went back to my parents' place to eat the oysters my uncle had brought from the shellfish factory he worked at and to wonder why we only got together when someone died.

WE FOUND SOME WONDERFUL LETTERS OF LIZZIE'S, HOW SHE WENT SKINNY-DIPPING ON KAPITI ISLAND & GOT CAUGHT AT IT BY BOYS

SHE WAS ADVENTUROUS

LEMON & SALT—THAT'S ALL YOU NEED

I'M AT RMIT

MOVE TO HOBOKEN— CHEAPER THAN NYC

BUT I WANT NYC!

IT'S A PITY LIZZIE ISN'T HERE TO ENJOY THIS— IT'S JUST HER KIND OF PARTY.

WE COULD ALWAYS HAVE A WEDDING SO WE COULD INVITE THE RELATIVES TO A HAPPY OCCASION

I THOUGHT WE WERE GOING TO GET MARRIED AT THE REGISTRY OFFICE

BUT WE HAVE TO HAVE A GOING-AWAY PARTY. WHY NOT HAVE A WEDDING / FAREWELL PARTY INSTEAD? WE CAN GET TRAVEL MONEY

THE IDEA OF A PROPER WEDDING MAKES ME FEEL UNCOMFORTABLE. WE'RE DOING IT FOR THE GREEN CARD,* RIGHT?

* I had a U.S. passport by birth & could sponsor Jonathan

I set about organising the wedding in 6 weeks. It was like putting on another fringe show.

On 31 august 2001 I had my last day at work.

On 1 September, my bridal cohort fêted me

And jonathan and I got married on the Wellington waterfront.

Halfway through the night, I sneaked out for a breather.

I'M SURE THAT GOOSE IS A SYMBOL OF GOOD LUCK

YOU THINK SO?

OH YES

MAYBE IT'S YOUR GRAN COMING TO CHECK OUT THE WEDDING PARTY

I ALWAYS THOUGHT GEESE WERE SILLY CREATURES.

OH NO! THEY GUARD THE WHISKY STILLS.

I was unconvinced by my aunt Mere's logic. What if it was a symbol of my big fat mistake? Was this a marriage of love or of visas?

We packed all our stuff the next few days  and stuck it in a storage locker.

We flew up to Auckland to finalise our visa application

and to spend the last few days chilling out with my family,

a TOAST TO NEW BEGINNINGS.

before we were due to move to New York City on September 17, 2001.

KNOCK KNOCK KNOCK

WAKE UP! WAKE UP NOW! SOMETHING TERRIBLE HAS HAPPENED.

COME DOWN AND WATCH THE TV — YOU WON'T BE ABLE TO GO TO NEW YORK NOW.

The planes did start flying to the U.S. again on the 17th.

Jonathan and I lined up to go through the New Security

and flew to the terrified new world.

218

In March 1918, still horribly ill, Katherine and Ida travelled to Paris. Katherine was determined to return to England to marry John, now that her divorce was finalised. Only you couldn't travel without permission during a war.

220

Katherine and Ida spent their days going from office to office, trying to procure a travel permit.

ANY LUCK?

SORRY MY DEAR. NO WORD FROM THE FRENCH

SO I'M STUCK IN THIS HELL HOLE?

AFRAID SO.

BOOM

WE'D BETTER GO TO THE CAVES, KATIE.

BOOM

BOOM

IF I WEREN'T SICK ALREADY I WOULD BE AFTER THIS

IF THERE ARE NO PERMITS DO YOU HAVE WORK? WE'RE OUT OF MONEY

WELL, THEY ARE IN NEED OF CANTEEN WORKERS AT THE GARE DU NORD

WE'LL TAKE IT— IT'S THAT OR STARVE HERE.

225

229

230

On 6 April, Katherine and Ida got permission to leave Paris.

and Katherine & Ida sailed for London on the 10th.

232

John and Katherine were married on 3 May, 1918, witnessed by Dorothy Brett and artist J. D. Fergusson.

WHY THE HANDKERCHIEF, JACK?

235

If I
can
make it
here

238

An american whom I'd
met in New Zealand
hooked us up with a
place to live - in Park
Slope, Brooklyn, with an
ex-high school friend of his.
Laura was also a graphic
designer, but she'd
lost her job in the dot
com bust. We took a car
service to her apartment,
and I felt like I was in a movie.

NEW
YORK IS A
GHOST TOWN.
EVERYBODY'S
HIDING

The room we were
meant to be renting
wasn't empty yet.

Dan'd been working as a web writer near
the towers when the planes hit. He'd seen
the people jumping.

He was moving to Baltimore.

Laura had been on her
way to   midtown

and she had to walk home, a trip that took
her hours, and shredded her felt.

240

241

STILL – LOOK WHERE I AM – I'M HERE, AT THE CENTRE OF THE WORLD, AFTER BEING ON THE EDGE FOR SO LONG.

AND NOW I'M DOING THE MANSFIELD THING – SEEING MY COUNTRY CLEARLY FROM A GREAT DISTANCE

I did find a job, to Laura's annoyance.

One of my workmates was a GQ model who had recently found religion

I JUST DON'T UNDERSTAND WHY THEY HATE US SO MUCH IN THE MIDDLE EAST – WE'RE THE GOOD GUYS

and another was an ageing extra from the 80s fratpack movies

I'M SORRY THAT YOU HAVE SO MANY BILLS, DANA, BUT NOW THAT YOU'RE NO LONGER AN EMPLOYEE OUR HEALTH INSURANCE DOESN'T COVER YOU.

DANA HAD YOUR JOB BUT NOW SHE'S ON BEDREST BECAUSE OF HER INCOMPETENT CERVIX SHE HAS PLENTY OF TIME TO RING ME UP & BUG ME. SHE'S PREGNANT WITH TWINS.

242

The company had once had 500 employees pre-dot.com bust, but now its core business was annual reports for big corporates. They wanted me to create a brochure and a website to promote their company, and they gave me 6 months.

I am SOOO BORED

I CAN'T BELIEVE THAT NYC IS THE CENTRE OF THE ART WORLD, BUT ALL OUR CLIENTS ARE BANKS AND MULTINATIONALS

It was a shock to me that I could be bored & dissatisfied...

I SUPPOSE IT'S ALSO THE CENTRE OF MONEY

...here, in the most exciting city in the world.

WHERE SHALL I GO FOR LUNCH TODAY?

I remembered the other maxim, you could go far away, but you'd always take yourself

MAYBE I NEED A WIG

and 'myself' wasn't really an impassioned corporate designer...

WHAT EVEN IS THIS JOOMUK-BAP?

I still wanted to be a writer or an artist

LUNCH TIME IS THE BEST PART OF THIS JOB

but then I wouldn't be able to afford to live here.

243

It turned out someone else at my work was also a writer.

I'm Marcia. I'm THE PROOFREADER. BUT I'm also a CHILDREN'S BOOK WRITER

OH, I'M A WRITER TOO!

WHAT KIND OF WRITER ARE YOU?

I WRITE SHORT STORIES— ONE WAS JUST PUBLISHED IN AN ANTHOLOGY— AND I'M PLANNING ON STARTING A NOVEL

CAN I SEE?

I gave her my book and she gave me hers

I HOPE THIS ISN'T TOO CRINGEY

THE MOONBRIDGE

I LIKED YOUR STORY— COULD I PHOTOCOPY IT AND SHOW IT TO MY WRITING GROUP? THEY'D LIKE A YOUNG PERSON TO JOIN

I was flattered that a real published author liked my work

YEAH, THAT'D BE GREAT— I'D LOVE SOME FEEDBACK. I LIKED YOUR BOOK TOO!

They gave me the ok & I set off to writing group one night.

244

I always felt anxious arriving at new places

Certain that I'd got the wrong time or day. The place looked fancy,

and I wondered who these people were, who truly belonged in NYC

YES, DEAR, THEY'RE UPSTAIRS WAITING FOR YOU

I was the youngest in the room by 25 years, and the oldest member was in his 80s. Doctors, psychotherapists, school principals—they all wrote on the side, although only a few had published

THERE'S NOTHING PRUDISH ABOUT THESE OLDER GUYS

JOSHUA DID NOT WANT TO COME OUT OF HIS TENT SO HE PEED IN EMPTY SODA BOTTLES. HE HAD 13 FLASKS FULL

Jonathan and I had moved into our own apartment a few blocks away from Laura's & we were enjoying a return to relative calm.

246

I was obsessed with the notion that I was infertile

My immune system had already taken out my pancreas so why not my ovaries too?

But the specialist didn't seem concerned

YOUR HbA1C IS 7 - YOU CAN MAKE BABIES IF YOU LIKE

I'LL GIVE YOU THE NUMBER OF a GREAT DIABETES NURSE

So one summer night, after a dinner party at a friend's...

WE HAD a HOME BIRTH EVEN THOUGH IT'S PRACTICALLY ILLEGAL HERE

THE MIDWIVES ARE SCARED OF BEING SUED

We went home

I'M SHO HOT & SHO DRUNK

YOU ARE SO HOT

NO BLOOD FOR OIL

DAMN THIS LOCK

FUMBLE FUMBLE

and didn't use condoms

I thought it would take years

I thought we'd probably have to use IVF, and that it would fail, but maybe by the time I was 38 I'd be bloated with hormones & pregnant with twins. and then I would lose them at 24 weeks.

I didn't think it would happen on our first try

only a few weeks into my new contract

250

HI, IS THAT LINDA? MY NAME IS SARAH. I'M ABOUT 6 WEEKS PREGNANT

I went to see the diabetes nurse in her Hell's Kitchen office

THIS IS NOT CONTROL. YOU ARE ALL OVER THE PLACE.

I'd been looking after myself all wrong for the past 20 years.

YOU KNOW ABOUT CARB COUNTING & BOLUSES? HERE'S A CHART. WE GOTTA CHANGE THAT INSULIN YOU'RE ON. HAVE YOU THOUGHT ABOUT A PUMP?

I found an OB-GYN, and wrangled my way onto an insurance plan for freelancers.

THERE YOU GO—A STRONG LITTLE HEARTBEAT. ACTIVE!

THANK GOD

I weighed my food and went for long walks & joined pregnancy yoga and had crazy disturbing dreams & fretted

WHAT IF THE BABY HAS A HOLE IN HIS HEART?

THE BABY WILL BE FINE

251

We arrived in Auckland in time for feijoa season

I found it hard to believe the baby would survive, so I didn't buy anything for it.

But then, when I hit 36 weeks, something happened.

And I was admitted to hospital.

and push...
until I had a baby.

Katherine was still thinking of her own lost baby when she moved into the Villa Isola Bella in Menton, France, in September 1920.

258

It was here that she wrote Miss Brill, The Stranger, & The Daughters of the Late Colonel

slipping in and out of a fever, Katherine dreamt.

KATHERINE, THERE YOU ARE — YOU MUST COME

GERTLER! BUT WHY?

I'VE GOT OSCAR WILDE THERE, HE'S THE MOST MARVELLOUS MAN I EVER MET

HE'S SO SHABBY

OSCAR, THIS IS MY DEAR FRIEND KATHERINE

KATHERINE, HELLO!

OH, OSCAR, I'VE ADORED YOU SINCE I WAS A GIRL IN WELLINGTON — PLEASE COME HOME WITH ME!

261

In December 1920, her collection of stories, "Bliss", was published to critical acclaim. John, who'd been working as an editor at the Athenaeum in London, came to visit, but it was fraught - the marital chastity was wearing on him, & he'd begun his affair with the young writer, Princess Bibesco.

I CAN SEE WHY IT SUITS YOU SO WELL HERE - THE PLACE IS CHARMING

I KNOW YOU'VE STILL GOT SOMETHING GOING ON WITH THAT RAPACIOUS GULL, BIBESCO

IT'S OVER, I PROMISE

THEN WHY DO ALL YOUR LETTERS KEEP DISAPPEARING? YOU USED TO LET ME READ THEM

SHE'S YOUNG - SHE'S INFATUATED. I'VE RESISTED HER ATTENTIONS AS BEST I CAN

RESIST A LITTLE HARDER!

I HAVE NEEDS, WIG.

SO DO I

BUT THESE DAYS, I'M A WRITER FIRST, A WOMAN SECOND. YOU CAN'T ASK MORE OF ME

The love letter from Princess Bibesco kept coming.

I CAN'T STAND IT THAT I AM REDUCED TO THIS. HE SWORE NOTHING ON EARTH WOULD COME BETWEEN US

VILLA ISOLA BELLA
GARAVAN
MENTON A/M

24
Jan
1921

Dear Princess Bibesco
I am afraid you must stop those little love letters to my husband while he and I live together. It is one of the things which is not done in our world.
You are my young. Would you ask your husband to explain to you impossibility of such a situat
Please do not mak write to you as a people and manners

And Katherine grew sicker, undergoing tubercular gland-draining.

FOLLOW ME, MADAME

which was painful & ineffective

265

As more tubercular swellings appeared, Katherine's writing intensified – both in her stories and her journal.

REMEMBER THOSE AUTOGRAPH BOOKS, THAT OVER-USED INSCRIPTION. "To thine own self be true"?

How dull it was, how boring to have the same advice written six times over. And then, even if it was Shakespeare that didn't prevent it – oh, l' d'innocence. From being dre obvious! Of the day that if True to oneself!

Which self? Which of my many – well really, that's what it's coming to – hundreds of selves?

concierge

...we are as intent as never before on trying to puzzle out, to live by our own particular self... Is it not possible that the rage for confession, autobiography, especially for memories of the earliest childhood, is explained by our persistent yet mysterious belief in a self which is continuous and permanent

untouched by all we acquire & all we shed pushes a green spear through the mould,

...we are alive, we are flowering for our moment on earth

This is the moment which, after all, we live for,
the moment of direct feeling when we are most
ourselves and least personal.

Lovely,
Unforgettable
Earth

The first 3 months were hell.

In the odd moments that the baby slept, I had to express.

Jonathan's mother came to visit, her cancer in abeyance.

And my mother was filled with well-meaning advice.

Jonathan got a job in Wellington & we moved next door to a pigeon lady.

Even though it was only 10 minutes from the central city, I felt like I was in the middle of nowhere.

As Otto began to feed & sleep better, I returned to my novel

I also started drawing a diary comic.

I'd just read "Persepolis" by Marjane Satrapi

and I remembered comics was something I once did.

My neighbour would make frequent appearances in it.

273

I thought I'd never finish my novel

But then I did.

YUSS

I gave my manuscript to my friends to read

I REALLY HOPE THEY LIKE IT

I'd sent a copy to Helen, and she invited us to her place for New Year's, a few weeks later.

274

She'd scattered a wildflower seed mix in spring.

She had great plans for her vegetable garden.

SO... WHAT DID YOU THINK OF MY NOVEL?

I REALLY LOVED IT. YOU ARE SO CLEVER. I THOUGHT JEREMY WAS A GREAT CHARACTER & IT HAD AN AIR OF NEW ZEALAND FAIRY TALE...

THERE WERE A FEW THINGS THAT BUGGED ME

My new year's resolution: to revise & perfect the novel

I spent another month working on it

find "cup cake"

I asked a literary assistant friend if I could send it to her.

TYPE TYPE TYPE

She worked at Writers House in NYC

She said yes

mama?

I sent it off on the 29th of January

DAIRY

New Zealand Post

IS THAT A GOOD OMEN OR A BAD OMEN?

Week DOMINION POST WRITER JANET FRAME DIES, 79

POSTAGE TO USA, PLEASE

YANK

GOODBYE

post

I went back to work in February

It was a good day if I arrived at 9am

Every morning I'd check my email before I did anything else. The New York emails came while I was sleeping.

But the bidding war seemed to elude me.

WAAAH! NOBODY WANTS MY NOVEL

REJECTION EMAILS, JONATHAN

MORE REJECTION EMAILS

MY NOVEL SUCKS. I'M A FAILURE.

YOU'RE NOT A FAILURE

YES I AM. I DON'T HAVE THAT X-FACTOR

YOU JUST HAVEN'T FOUND THE RIGHT PUBLISHER YET

I WASTED ALL THAT TIME

NO YOU DIDN'T

I HAVE NO TALENT

And now Jonathan's mother really was dying.

I'VE GOT TO GO UP NORTH

MUM'S NOT HAVING ANY MORE CHEMO. SHE'S GOING ONTO PALLIATIVE CARE

THEY SAY SHE'S ONLY GOT A FEW MONTHS

Dying seemed to be a fitful affair

and although I knew I needed to treasure this time

I wished that something would happen, because our lives were in limbo.

Perhaps I was a bad person. I was definitely going to write a short story about this.

WE SHOULD HAVE ANOTHER BABY. I'M NOT SURE I'M SUITED TO THIS PARENTING BUSINESS, BUT I DON'T WANT OTTO TO BE AN ONLY CHILD.

WELL, IT'S NOT AS IF I CAN SLEEP ANYWAY

I got pregnant as she died, not that I knew it at the time.

and if there was such thing as an afterlife.

Again fuelled by pregnancy hormones, I worked on my writing. I'd abandonned my novel & a pregnancy memoir and was trying to get a collection of short stories together, even though I knew that- despite Katherine Mansfield - short stories didn't sell.

It was vital that I finish this before the baby came.

Freezer gum

This time I was going to surrender myself to motherhood

and not fight it, as I had with Otto.

TAKE OUR PICTURE NOW, DADDY!

The baby came before I was done

WELLING

HELLO, GUS

282

and if I'd thought parenting was busy before, it truly was now.

I was too restless and ambitious

unable to zen out

285

LOOK AT MT RUAPEHU

We dropped Otto off with my parents

GOOD LUCK! HAVE FUN!

& we took a taxi to the hotel.

WHAT A GIANT BED

PITY YOUR PARENTS COULDN'T TAKE GUS AS WELL

Once the babysitter arrived, we went downstairs to join the other finalists in the lobby.

I am SO FREAKING NERVOUS I might EXPLODE. AND THAT'S OWEN MARSHALL. I STUDIED HIM IN SCHOOL.

YOU'LL WIN THIS TIME. I KNOW

I hoped that I would win, because I would probably cry in public if I didn't.

SARAH! SO NICE TO MEET YOU

The prime minister gave a speech

It was past feeding time - my boobs were aching and by the time I got back to my hotel room I was tired and drunk.

288

I didn't sleep a wink.

I returned to Wellington with renewed enthusiasm.

I dreamt that I was sitting in a garden on Tinakori Road with my grandmother. I was filled with a sense of bliss, and that this was more than a dream - it was a visitation.

I decided to call the collection "Coming Up Roses", partly after the dream, and also after a story. I spent ages deciding their order.

I got the email a few weeks later, just before christmas

omg, IT'S FROM RANDOM HOUSE

To: Sarah Laing
From: █████ █████
Subject: Coming Up

Dear Sarah

Well, I've just got c
publishing committe
thrilled to tell you
accepted for publ
July 2007, I hop

I was 34 years when I had my first book of short stories published. The age Katherine Mansfield was when she died.

In August 1922, Katherine returned to Hampstead to stay with Brett.

One of the first visitors was Orage, Katherine's editor at The NEW AGE, from her early days in London.

Ouspensky was lecturing about Gurdjieff's Institute for the Harmonious Development of Man

WE DO NOT KNOW THAT WE HAVE NOT ONE "I" BUT MANY DIFFERENT "I"'S CONNECTED WITH OUR FEELINGS & DESIRES AND HAVE NO CONTROLLING "I"'S

THESE "I"'S CHANGE ALL THE TIME; ONE SUPRESSES ANOTHER, ONE REPLACES ANOTHER AND ALL THIS STRUGGLE MAKES UP OUR INNER LIVES

Katherine and Ida arrived at the Institute on 16 October, 1922

300

301

302

YOU KNOW, ORAGE, I'VE REALISED SOMETHING. UP UNTIL NOW I'VE BEEN A CAMERA - A VERY 'SELECTIVE' CAMERA

HOW SO, KATYA?

MY 'SLICES OF LIFE' HAVE BEEN PARTIAL, MISLEADING AND A LITTLE MALICIOUS AND GOD KNOWS I ENCOURAGED THAT FROM THE BEGINNING

I WANT TO WIDEN THE SCOPE OF MY CAMERA - TO NOT REPRESENT LIFE AS IT MERELY APPEARS

BUT WITH A TRULY CREATIVE ATTITUDE

I COULD NOT WRITE MY OLD STORIES AGAIN - MY ATTITUDE HAS CHANGED, AND THE PATTERNS ARE DIFFERENT

AN ARTIST COMMUNICATES NOT HIS VISION OF THE WORLD BUT THE ATTITUDE WHICH RESULTS IN HIS VISION

NOT HIS DREAM, BUT HIS DREAM STATE. WHAT I'M TRYING TO SAY IS THAT IF WRITERS HAD A NEW ATTITUDE, THEY WOULD FIRST SEE LIFE DIFFERENTLY AND THEN MAKE IT DIFFERENT

306

314

I seen the

little lamp

I thought I'd be satisfied after I'd published a book. After all, I was a "real writer" now.

IT'S REALLY REAL

LET ME SEE

SO WHAT DID YOU THINK?

WELL, THERE WERE MOMENTS OF BRILLIANCE — BUT REALLY, I THINK YOU OVER-EGGED IT. AND THERE WERE STORIES YOU SHOULD'VE JUST LEFT OUT.

STILL, YOU HAVE TIME...

UNLIKE ME.

LOOK, YOU MAY NOT HAVE GOT IT RIGHT WITH THE SHORT STORIES, BUT THERE'S ALWAYS THE NOVEL. DO YOU HAVE AN IDEA FOR ANOTHER NOVEL?

As a matter of fact I did. Every night, after I put the kids to bed, I went into my office and typed 300 more words about a diabetic cellist moving to New York City.

I was perplexed by my ambition.

My fame fantasy was one of escapism—I imagined having an apartment in New York City, one in Paris. I dreamed of having a full-time au pair. Instead, we moved to Auckland, where my mother promised to babysit.

I liked being able to swim in the sea without flinching, even though we sometimes found condoms on the beach.

I was invited back to Wellington, to a writers' festival, in which I had to write & perform a story in a day.

and the bag-pipes squalled

THIS IS EXCRUTIATING

I ran into an old friend of my mother's, who'd become a famous writer

IT'S GREAT TO SEE YOU HERE AS A FELLOW WRITER — I'M SO PROUD

IT'S EXCITING TO BE HERE

IT'S FUNNY, THIS WRITING IMPULSE. IT'S LIKE WE NEVER WANTED TO GIVE UP PLAYING WITH OUR DOLL'S HOUSES, REARRANGING THE ROOMS & PUTTING THE DOLLS INTO COMPROMISING POSITIONS

YES! THAT'S IT!

PERHAPS MY WRITING ISN'T DRIVEN BY A DESIRE FOR FAME. PERHAPS I JUST WANT TO BE IN CONTROL OF MY OWN LITTLE UNIVERSES

I was pregnant with my 3rd child when my novel was launched.

DO I LOOK FAT IN THIS DRESS?

YOU LOOK HUGE!

PREGNANCY'S THE ONLY TIME I SUIT GRANNY'S GREEN ORGANZA.

and the anxiety of the pregnancy almost—not quite—distracted me from the reviews

CLICHÉ?! WHAT ARE THEY TALKING ABOUT?

I didn't write for 9 months after Violet was born, but I drew comics

I applied for a fellowship in anticipation of the time when I could leave Violet in daycare

and amazingly, I got it.

Finally, I had a room of my own!

This time round, I wasn't going to write anything semi-autobiographical.

I was going to create an entirely fictional world.

Any autobiographical impulse I'd channel into my comics.

I created my own little microcosm, a collection of doll's houses in which I could play with my characters.

My mother preferred this approach. My friend Drew was not so sure

I THINK THIS NOVEL IS YOUR BEST YET. YOUR LAST ONE MADE ME FEEL UNCOMFORTABLE READING about you

BUT IT WAS FICTION, mum

I JUST DIDN'T WARM TO YOUR LATEST NOVEL, SARAH. I LOVED 'DEAD PEOPLE'S MUSIC!' WRITE ANOTHER ONE LIKE THAT.

I'd got pretty good reviews this time round—it cut me up that it wasn't universally admired.

DON'T MY FRIENDS GET THAT I CAN'T KEEP WRITING THE SAME THING OVER AND OVER?

Why should I have to be liked by everyone anyway? I needed to cultivate an "I don't give a damn" attitude.

HAVE YOU GOT YOUR BOOK BAG & BRAIN SNACK OUT?

NOW, LET'S DROP YOU OFF AT KINDY SO MUMMY CAN GO HOME AND DRAW COMICS

DRAW COMICS WITH ME AT KINDY?

We moved back to Wellington seven years after shifting north

BUT I LIKE IT HERE— I'M ESTABLISHED —I DON'T WANT TO MOVE BACK

THIS JOB IS MUCH BETTER FOR ME—I'LL GET A RAISE TOO

I SHOULD'VE STAYED BEING A FULL-TIME GRAPHIC DESIGNER— THEN I COULD'VE CALLED THE SHOTS

I'd planned on finding us a new house in Island Bay, Newtown, Lyall Bay — somewhere a little bohemian.

THIS PLACE IS AMAZING— BUT IT'S IN KARORI

KARORI, KARORI, HOW MY HEART BEATS FOR KARORI. BESIDES—AREN'T YOU JEALOUS OF PEOPLE WITH HISTORICAL CONNECTIONS TO PLACES? FOUR GENERATIONS OF YOUR FAMILY HAVE LIVED HERE.

MY GRANDMOTHER SAID YOU LIVED DOWN THE ROAD. BUT YOU LIVED MILES AWAY.

We moved in early February, just in time for the children to start at the local school

I LOVE THIS HOUSE— THIS IS MY FOREVER HOUSE

LOOK, MUM — A PLAQUE ABOUT KATHERINE MANSFIELD

LET ME TAKE A PHOTO OF THIS

TO THE MEMORY OF
KATHLEEN MANSFIELD BEAU
KATHERINE MANSFIELD
WHO COMMENCED HER EDUCA
THIS SCHOOL 1895-1898 AND LAT
ACHIEVED A WORLDWIDE REPUTAT
AS A WRITER OF SHORT STORIES-
BORN WELLINGTON-14 OCTOBER
DIED FONTAINEBLEAU FRANC

Gus liked to play underneath the stand of pine & macrocarpa, where he made little houses out of sticks.

...the same stand of trees that Kezia, Isabel and Lottie held court under, in Katherine's story, "The Doll's House."

Everyone was invited except for the Kelveys, the daughters of a washerwoman and an absent father.

The other children were not allowed to talk to the Kelveys

Thank you!

THANK YOU TO THE UNIVERSITY OF AUCKLAND AND THE MICHAEL
KING WRITERS CENTRE, WHERE I FIRST BEGAN WORK ON THIS BOOK
AS A WRITER IN RESIDENCE, FEELING LIKE A REAL WRITER WITH A
SALARY AND A ROOM OF MY OWN. THANKS TO KIM MEEK AND MIRIAM
HARRIS, WHO PROVIDED FEEDBACK AS I DEVELOPED THE MANUSCRIPT,
AND TO SCOTT WILSON, DYLAN HORROCKS, WELBY INGS AND PETER
MADDEN, WHO READ IT AT VARIOUS STAGES AND GAVE ME HOPE.
THANK YOU TO JO EMENEY, WHO DELIVERED A BUNDLE OF
MANSFIELD BOOKS, AND PROOF-READ FOR ME AT THE END.
THANK YOU TO DAVID COLQUHOUN, FOR HUNTING OUT MANSFIELD
TREASURES IN THE ARCHIVES, AND INCLUDING PAGES OF THE
MANUSCRIPT IN THE CAPITAL CHARACTERS EXHIBITION.
THANK YOU TO ADRIAN KINNAIRD, KELLY SHEEHAN AND DAMON KEEN,
WHO ALSO GAVE ME REASON TO BELIEVE IT MIGHT BECOME A REAL
BOOK. THANKS TO THE LOVELY PEOPLE AT VUP: FERGUS BARROWMAN,
ASHLEIGH YOUNG, KIRSTEN McDOUGALL, CRAIG GAMBLE, HOLLY HUNTER,
AND KYLEIGH HODGSON FOR USHERING THIS BOOK INTO THE WORLD
AND GIVING IT A SPINE. THANKS TO ELIZABETH KNOX FOR YOUR KIND
WORDS AND SUPPORT. THANK YOU TO HELEN LEHNDORF AND DREW
BARNETT, BFFS 4EVA, AND THANK YOU TO MY SISTER, MELISSA LAING,
FOR ON-GOING WISE COUNSEL. THANKS TO MY PARENTS, WILLIAM AND
ROBYN LAING, FOR ALWAYS ENCOURAGING ME IN THE ARTS, AND FOR
BABYSITTING MY CHILDREN. THANK YOU, TIM! YOU HELPED TOO!
MOST OF ALL, THANK YOU TO JONATHAN LANE, WHO HAS READ MY
SCRIBBLY DRAFTS AND MORE REFINED COMICS AT EVERY STAGE AND
HAS BEEN AN INSIGHTFUL AND ENTHUSIASTIC READER. THANK YOU
TO MY CHILDREN: OTTO, GUS, AND VIOLET (WHO THINKS I SHOULD GIVE
UP BEING A WRITER AND BECOME A ZOOKEEPER INSTEAD).

Author's Note

Although much of Katherine Mansfield's dialogue has been invented, I have also drawn on sources. I'm indebted to the biographies that I read: Antony Alpers' THE LIFE OF KATHERINE MANSFIELD, Kathleen Jones' KATHERINE MANSFIELD: THE STORY-TELLER and Claire Tomalin's KATHERINE MANSFIELD: A SECRET LIFE. I referred to both the 1930 and the 1951 editions of Mansfield's letters, edited by John Middleton Murry, and I scoured Margaret Scott's THE KATHERINE MANSFIELD NOTEBOOKS. Many of the stories quoted come from the Random House 2007 edition, KATHERINE MANSFIELD'S SHORT STORIES. I reconstructed the Fontainebleau sequence from Olgivanna's account, THE LAST DAYS OF KATHERINE MANSFIELD, and Orage's essay, TALKS WITH KATHERINE MANSFIELD at FONTAINEBLEAU. I also found the collection of photos at Digital NZ very helpful, along with Mansfield's actual letters and journals held within the Alexander Turnbull Library Collection.

Sarah Laing was born in Champaign-Urbana in 1973 to New Zealand parents, and grew up in Palmerston North. The winner of the 2006 Sunday Star Times Short Story Competition, she went on to publish a collection of stories and two novels. She was awarded fellowships at the Michael King Writers Centre, the Sargeson Centre and the University of Auckland. Also a graphic designer and illustrator, she's contributed comics to magazines, illustrated children's books and co-edited Three Words: An ANthology of Aotearoa/NZ Women's Comics. She lives in Wellington with her family. You can follow her on her blog: sarahelaing.com, or on Twitter or Instagram: @sarahelaing